Usborne

First Colouring Book
Pirates

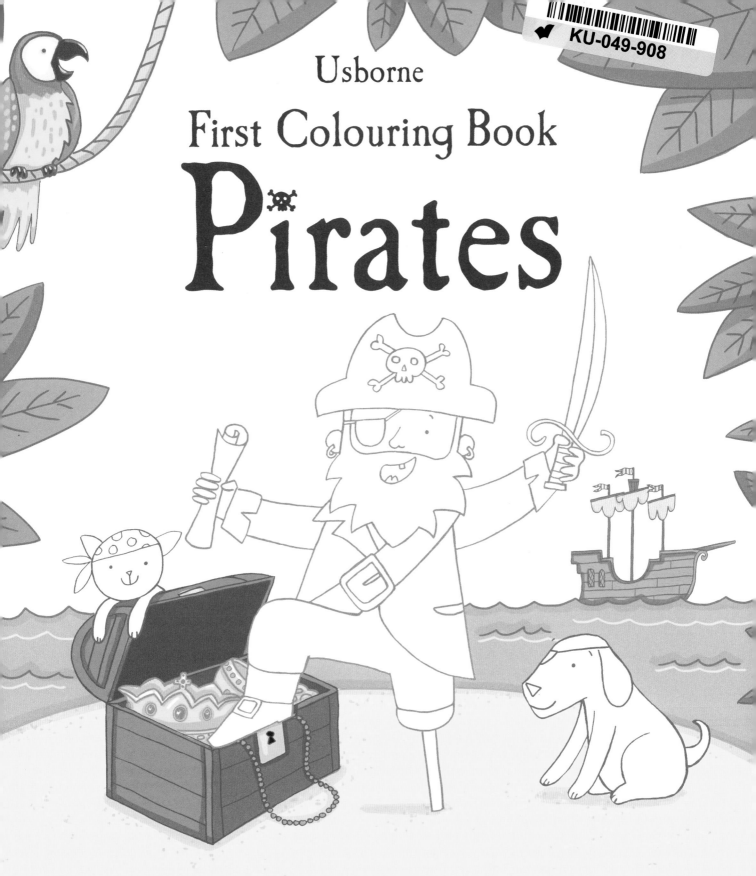

This book belongs to

- - - - - - - - - - - - - -

The pirate gang

Captain Crayfish and his gang of crafty pirates are about to set sail in their ship, The Jolly Dolphin. They're in search of buried treasure!

Meet the crew

Say hello to some of the people and animals on board the pirate ship.

Jim, the deckhand

Captain Crayfish

Pirate flag

"Sharp-eyes" Jack, the lookout

Gaptooth Stan, the anchor man

Caspar, the ship's cat

Percy the parrot

Salty the sea dog

Penny the pirate

Burns, the ship's cook

Treasure map

This is the pirates' treasure map.
Use your pens or crayons to finish it.

On the high seas

The Jolly Dolphin sails through the crashing waves, searching for the treasure island.

Land ahoy!

Now the pirates have spotted an island.
Could this be where the treasure is buried?

Digging for gold

On the island, the pirates follow their treasure map to find the right place to dig. It looks as though they've found something ...

Pirate party

Everyone on the ship celebrates their find with a jolly pirate dance in the moonlight.

Treasure!

Look what the pirates found... the chest was full to the brim with gold, silver and sparkling jewels.